WAITING FOR JESUS

Stories and prayers
by
Hilary Faith Jones

illustrations
by
Eddie Askew

Published by The Leprosy Mission International

All rights and subsidiary rights have been granted to
The Leprosy Mission International
80 Windmill Road
Brentford
Middlesex TW8 0QH, United Kingdom

Please see page 99 for address and contact details.

Published in 2001
A catalogue record for this book is available from the British Library
Printed and bound in Spain by Bookprint, S.L. - Barcelona
ISBN 0 902731 44 0

Cover illustration: SUMMER IN NORWAY, pastel
Illustration above: "AND NO BIRDS SING" WINTER, watercolour

For Nichola –

who taught me the laughter of Christ

Books of meditations, Bible readings and prayers by Eddie Askew,
published by The Leprosy Mission International:

A Silence and A Shouting	*Disguises of Love*
Many Voices One Voice	*No Strange Land*
Facing the Storm	*Breaking the Rules*
Cross Purposes	*Slower than Butterflies*
Music on the Wind	*Edge of Daylight*

Other books published by The Leprosy Mission International:
Awakenings by Hilary Faith Jones
The Song of the Sparrow by Alison Stedman

Famous books by Paul Brand:

Ten Fingers for God	*Granny Brand*
The Gift of Pain	*Fearfully and Wonderfully Made*

All of the above books are available direct from:
TLM TRADING LIMITED
PO Box 212, Peterborough, PE2 5GD
Tel: 01733 239252, Fax: 01733 239258
E-mail: tlmtrading@dial.pipex.com

Pauline Webb is a writer and broadcaster who frequently presents the Daily Service on BBC Radio 4 and Pause for Thought on Radio 2. She is a former Vice-President of the Methodist Conference and was the first woman to be elected as Vice-Moderator of the World Council of Churches. Until her retirement she worked as Head of Religious Broadcasting in the BBC World Service. She is a Methodist local preacher well-known in the ecumenical world. She has written several books on spiritual topics, the most recent of which, *Worship in Every Event* (pub. OUP) is concerned with the leading of relevant worship and personal prayer.

Foreword

The gospel writers give us many tantalising glimpses into the lives of people whose paths at some point in their lives crossed the path of Jesus. We are left wondering what led up to that encounter and what impact it had upon the rest of their lives. In this book, Hilary Faith Jones, with the skill of an experienced story-teller, takes us into their innermost thoughts as they approach this most important encounter. She echoes for us the kind of conversation they may have had with Jesus. Through these pages we come to feel that we know personally what it was like to wait, as Simeon and Anna waited, right up until their old age to see the promises of God fulfilled. We share the embarrassment of the woman at the well as she meets a stranger who seems to know her better than she knows herself. We even experience what it is like to come right to the margin of death as the young daughter of Jairus recalls how Jesus brought her back to life, speaking to her in words of haunting, poetic beauty.

The stories are so vividly written that they enable us to identify ourselves with the Biblical characters, and to recognise in their experiences our own feelings of joy or sorrow, of doubt or faith, of gratitude or penitence. They move naturally from narrative to prayer. Each of the stories leads into a brief but deeply moving cry from the heart which expresses a personal devotion in prayer. These could also be used most effectively in public worship as people are encouraged to meditate upon the stories we read in the gospels and link them with our own stories.

Hilary's writing comes from the pen not only of a poet but also of one who has learned to express the deep longings of the soul in the language of both poetry and prayer. For that reason I believe this book could become a classic for both personal and public devotional reading. I warmly commend it to all who long to come, like the people of the gospel stories, closer into the company of Jesus.

Pauline Webb

Contents

The Recognition

These last weeks had been full of uncertainties.
The old man wondered if his time was close,
for there was a disturbing restlessness within him.
He quietly left his home
carefully made his way through the streets,
stopping and sharing with all who called him,
glad of the breeze
that calmed his searching thoughts.

He climbed to the Temple,
gathering his thinking into prayer –
but still
his soul could not settle.
He moved to the space of the great pillars
hoping the air would help
and watched, puzzling, the faces of those
who came and went.
Saw the couple toil up the steps,
the girl tiring, handing the baby to her husband.
And it was then, as she passed the child over,
that the girl looked up
and caught the old man's gaze.

And suddenly a great fire burned through him.

He moved slowly forward to intercept them;
they stopped for him –
respectful of his age and frail dignity.
He forced himself to study their faces,
everything within him longing to look at the child
but knowing he had to be right.
And he found truth, honesty, faith.

Slowly, oh so slowly
his hand reached forward
and touched the shawl that edged the child's head.
And with profound understanding
the husband gently offered
the days-old baby to the man of God.

Transfixed,
the old man held the Christ-child within his arms,
terrified at the awesomeness
yet with dawning insight at the baby's warmth,
the smell of sweetness
the perfection of the tiny nails.
Truly one of us.

Gently, oh so gently,
he kissed the soft down on the baby's head
and when the old man lifted up his eyes
his face was shining,
as if he had already
stepped across to heaven.

And thus God's grace
flowed through him,
to touch upon the girl and husband,
whilst the child slept,
curled into the arms of the old.

And unhindered
God's blessing
seemed to ripple on
through the Temple
to touch upon the tiny prophetess
nearly blind with years
and twisted with shrunken bones.

She felt it, sensed it –
and limped towards the entrance
where the generations of God
gathered.

Her hands,
dark blue veins painfully threading together
the paper skin,
delicately whispered over the face of the girl and her husband
before, trembling,
she touched the air above the baby's head.
Her fingers fluttered to her own lips –

> *Oh Simeon*
> *the waiting is over.*
> *He is the One.*

And for a moment, together,
the old foresaw eternity.

Later, as she was leaving,
the girl turned back briefly
to see the silhouette of an old man and an old woman
standing hand in hand
like little children,
on the threshold of heaven.

God of the unexpected
May your wisdom grow in me

God of surprises
May your vision work within me

God of wonder
May your grace flow through me
as I stand
each day
on the threshold of your heaven.

HRADCANY, PRAGUE, *watercolour*

The Desert Waiting

The sun reached its height.
Blazed down with a relentless fury that blinded;
burnt the delicate skin on the top of the head,
scorched the soles of the feet.

She pulled back from the intensity,
reluctant to leave the coolness of the house,
to move from darkness to oppressive light.
Staggering as the suffocation of heat smothered her,
she kept her eyes shielded from the piercing glare
that beat between the houses,
and gradually made her way to the edge of the city.
Stepped through the shadows
moved listlessly from dark to light,
shadow to sun.
Finally stepped from the last blackness
into the full blaze of the desert –
a shimmering vast expanse
where macabre figures twisted into nothing.

Thought he was one such figure
sometimes there, sometimes not –
a distortion of reality in the shade of the well.

She sensed rather than saw him watching her.
And suddenly she was tired.
Tired of the innuendoes, the constant exclusion,
the whole act she had to go through each time.
Inside she sighed,
longed to be left alone.

She straightened and, squinting in the light, stared back at him.

As his face fell in shadow it was difficult to read him.
Yet still she met his gaze openly
giving herself time to measure him –
waiting to see if he would speak.
He slowly indicated the well.
Asked her for a drink.

The game had started.

Nonchalantly she looked away, seemingly deliberating,
A Jew asking a Samaritan?
A man asking a woman? she murmured.
Lazily bringing her gaze back to his face.

His eyes hadn't moved.
If you only knew the gift of God.
If you only knew who is asking you,
then you would do the asking
and he would let you drink living water.

She was surprised.
Hadn't expected this.
Couldn't tell whether he was rebuking her
or merely being amusing.
Whatever it was,
she was rather intrigued.
None of the men she knew ever spoke like this.

She leant on the well, enjoying herself.
Living water, eh? You can't even draw the water yourself.
She shot him a quick look and smiled,
You wouldn't be putting yourself above our father Jacob
who actually gave us the well now, would you?

She waited for him to laugh,
to realise that he had been caught out.
To recognise that although she was a woman,
she was also smart.

But he surprised her again.
And this time she sensed the seriousness beneath the words.
If you drink here,
you will be thirsty again.
But if you drink the water I give you,
it will be like ...
he paused and she felt he was searching for words
that she would understand,
...it will be like a spring of water welling up to eternal life.

She was strangely touched.
For a moment she went still.
Found it quite beautiful.

She was both moved but unsure.
And when uncertain it was safer to retreat.
Give me that water and I won't be thirsty –
save me coming here again!
She started to laugh it off
but found herself longing to have grasped
something of the beauty that had
momentarily filled the desert.

But he took her seriously.
Go and bring your husband.
His voice was no different
and yet the air moved as if a tremendous
power was being released.

Immediately,
everything within her panicked.
So unexpected
there had been no warning,
no time to prepare.
She had suddenly been propelled to the edge.
Her heart began to pound so fiercely that
she thought her head would burst.
The pain in her heart, her head, her veins
became explosive.

She hadn't known that one could feel so
desperately, deeply sick.
Grief and guilt bludgeoned inside her,
threatened to burst out.

Under the terrifying glare of the sun,
the relentlessness of killing heat,
she stood held in time.
Was vaguely aware that this moment
would last as long as she needed;
was only very dimly aware
that what was happening would change the future,
would change races and creeds and ideologies,
would transform the togetherness of woman and man.

She could lie – and step back
or she could tell the truth – and lose him.

The agony of the decision terrified her.
The agony of bringing the past to the present
the agony of guilt and hope
despair and longing
ripped her open.

And then it was –
through the stinging distortion of her vision,
through the blurred and indecipherable images,
that he came quite clearly into focus.
And she glimpsed, fleetingly, in his eyes,
the mirror
of her own soul –
full of pain and grief and sorrow.

Or maybe,
she was a reflection of a fraction of
the pain that he carried.

She struggled for breath –
and stepped forward.
  I have no husband.

The truth exploded inside her,
split and splintered her.

His voice came,
oh, so gently.

  I know, he whispered again
and again.

  I know.
A great heavy wave of forgiveness
broke over her,
filled her,
moved through her.

And eventually,
she looked straight at him
and her eyes were clear of the past.
Why was this man so full of the unexpected?

And then he smiled.
Understood where she was,
her confusion to step where she had not been shown.

So he talked with her.
Sitting on the scorched ground
he told her about God.
And as he talked
she began to understand.
Watching her face,
he saw the connections begin to take place.
Saw his gift of wisdom
sparking inside her.
She talked to him of the Messiah,
slowly starting to put the brilliance together.
And as she spoke,
she looked at him with eyes that gradually
became huge,
silent with wonder.

Yes! he laughed.
I am He!

You are He! she whispered,
as His laughter filled her.

You are He!
Her hands reached out and caught His.

You are He!
She leapt to her feet and flung back her arms and face to the piercing sky.

You are He!! she shouted.
And together their laughter filled the wasteland.

Sensing the mirage of men approaching,
her hair tumbling around her,
she picked up her skirts
and ran like the wind over the fire of the sand,
laughter from Him chasing and catching her.
Powerful and vibrant
her voice echoed down the stirring streets.

And so she called her excluders
to share the wonder
that was waiting in the desert.

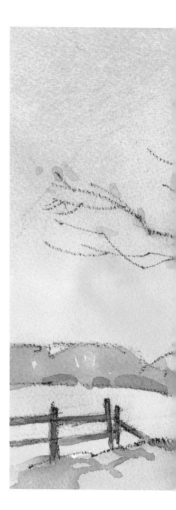

The forgiveness of Christ
fills me

The love of Christ
heals me

The laughter of Christ
surrounds me

Now my soul sings in wonder.
Glory be to God!

A SUMMER RENDEZVOUS, *watercolour*

A Matter of Minutes

Warm wall against my back.
Rough stones
whose crevices my fingers
have travelled
time and time again
in the wearying length of day.

Dusty earth
where my feet
draw patterns
in unending forms,
to be scuffed
and dissipated to the winds.

Piercing heat of sun,
causing sharp
flickerings in my mind;
makes me wince
and hold my hands clenched tight
against the sockets of my face.

Feel the rhythm of the passing feet,
hear the fragments of the talk,
live desperately the lives of those
who flit
across
my sense-filled,
senseless world.

Heard them approaching.
Heavy feet, easy walk,
voices questioning.

Into beggar form.
Hand outstretched, head tilted,
eyes upward, rolling pointlessly,
whining voice slicing across their thoughts.
Feet stop.

Too close.
Feel their clothing brushing against my skin,
smell the presence of too many men.
Suffocating,
airless,
know what's going to happen next.

Body snaps instinctively.
Tight ball, my fists into my eyes,
must protect,
must protect.
Lights in the head start to burst in agony.
Hold the breathing –
wait for the pain,
for the terror,
for the heat of the blood.

Only sound the roaring of heart inside head.
A matter of minutes.
A matter of minutes.
Suddenly feel space around.
Sense the coolness in the air.
Become aware in the dust-choked breath
of a man on the ground.
Fingers gently touching, travelling across my face,
exploring
seeking
searching.
Discovering too much.

Somehow,
he feels the torture inside my head;
feels the jagged pain reverberating.

Warm wet mud
against my hollow bones.
Pull back
fear-filled,
but he holds me close,
his fingers speak of trust.
Held within his arms
the lights inside begin to slow
until
at last
the deepest darkness lies unbroken.

And now he speaks
and his voice is slow and strong.
Sound that burns, deep into my bones.
Stagger up.
Know I must obey.
But –
something pulls me back.
Kneel yet again in my squalid earth
and there,
surrounded by the familiar,
I run my fingers –
once only –
across his face.

Then I am gone,
fingers flying along the wall,
hurtling to the market pool,
counting my steps along its edge.
Slip and slither into its depths.

Icy wet body
shivering uncontrollably
both out
and in.
Final look into the darkness
then plunge the hands and heave the water,
slapping away the caking mud.

Sense a different feeling between the screwed up lashes.
Force them open.

Light pours through.
Body-shattering pain.
The agony of such strength,
such intense hurt,
such force
breaks my delight.
But then I discover along the pain,
such immeasurable beauty,
such shot-through iridescence
such staggering depth, vastness, richness.
Such untold profundity.

Heart-held moment.

It is only later that it dawns on me.
Perhaps the gift of seeing,
blinds the sighted to what is so mysteriously transparent.
For my fingers
told me what my eyes could not.
That,
just for a moment,
I had touched upon
the face of God.

O Jesus
When I am without sight
touch my vision
that I may see God's wonder
close beside me.

When I am filled with joy
let me hold your hand
that I may share with you.

When I am afraid
take me in your arms
and hold me fast.

And Jesus –
when I cannot see you
take my ordinary fingers
and let them travel
across your face.

For you are my all in all –
and I cannot live without you.

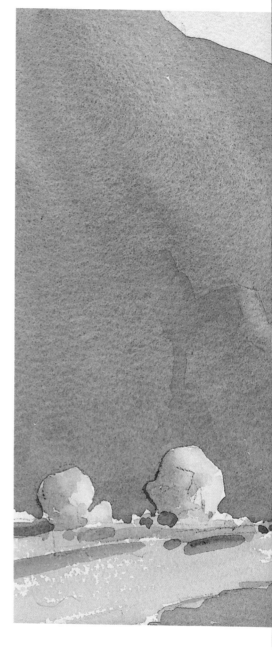

NORHEIMSUND, WESTERN FJORDS,
NORWAY, watercolour

Unseen Gift

The market place was frighteningly loud.
Clamour and noise ricocheted around the square
with the heaving, seething heat of the crowd.

Mary waited and watched,
took in all the movement and noise and bustle,
absorbed the faces that
chanced across her watching,
was aware of all that was
and all that would be.
And because she had the gift,
it was not the meanness nor the sharpness nor the shallowness
that left their impression
but the potential for God that she saw.

And suddenly life –
in the midst of the noise and the heat and the dust and the strangers –
was so good
that she wanted to fling back her head,
open her eyes to the sky
become one with the noise of the people
and one with the stillness of nature
and let her soul fly.

Martha watched her returning.
Felt the strange mixture of
protective love mingle with irritation.

As children she had been the dominant one,
protecting Mary and their brother
from the buffeting of life.
As adults it was Martha who made the decisions,
who had her feet planted solidly in reality
and was ruthlessly perceptive in her assessment of men.

It was Martha
who created the home that kept them together.

And why?
Because this was her dream.

Not to see beyond –
but to be ready in the now and the immediate.
This was her pleasure
to see the whiteness of the cloth;
her delight
in the opening of her home, her hearth, her love –
so that all were welcome.
The now.
The present.

And somehow,
it was because she was the Martha of reality,
that the brother and sister were enabled to be free.

She watched Mary stop in the orchard,
pausing to push her hair from her face,
a face uplifted in child-like pleasure as the sun slanted across it.
A face of innocence.

Lazarus was different – he was a man.
But Mary was as herself –
and again that mixture
of pride and frustration heated through Martha,
knotted in her stomach.

She loved her sister's fragile beauty,
her vulnerability,
yet increasingly it gnawed at her
that sometimes Mary's sweetness of nature
appeared as weakness,
her dreaminess as indecision,
her strange ability to be in touch with the profound things in life
as an excuse to avoid the mundane.

The thoughts unclarified and unspoken
caused her to call more sharply than she had intended;
Mary heard the quickness of the voice
and her eyes flew to her sister's
uncertain as to what was wrong.
But Martha had already gone
and the discord was forgotten in the excitement and rush and speed
of last minute preparations.

The men's voices were heard,
carried clearly on the still dusk air,
and Martha turned excitedly to call to Mary –
only to discover that she had already gone –
her feet flying over stony ground,
laughing with delight as she ran into the teacher's arms
and held his hand like a little child.

And the tired group of men
was suddenly infused by
the spark and the fire
of souls joining in brilliance.

And briefly the knot tightened
inside Martha
and she turned quickly away.

Fingers that flew in creating,
hearts that were seeking,
bread that was warming.
The preparation was reaching its time for fulfilment.

And then
in the frantic push to provide the perfect,
Martha misjudged –
and as she rushed past the open door
the bread slipped from her red worn fingers
to scatter in the dust and dirt outside.

And her world, her dream, was over
and the frustrations knotted to unbelievable
proportions inside.
For a moment
life spun around her before internally
she snapped.

She stormed into the room
her face blazing from the anger that was
clenched inside
and somehow –
everything in life seemed to be Mary's fault
and everything was enormously unfair.

To everyone's amazement
Martha –
the solid, dependable one,
the predictable, prosaic, unemotional woman
suddenly exploded in rage.

Tears of anger and frustration
burnt her,
as all the grievances spilt out irrationally,
until she could speak no more
and her hands clenched in terrible pent-up agony
against the rigidity of her physical fury.

No one moved.
No one spoke.
Tears of terror flowed silently down Mary's face.

But the Teacher understood.

Understood the rage,
the complications and complexities of human relationships,
the struggle between love and letting go,
the difficulties in being unique and special
and believing it within your soul,
the longing to be recognised
and accepted
for the person you are.

So he held the furious woman
within his arms;
gently stroked her hair
as she collapsed and sobbed into him –
and loved her
and cherished her
and believed in her.

And when she was quiet,
when she had let go,
the teacher smiled beyond to Mary
who was waiting –
and Martha turned
and her soul was at peace
as she held out her hands
to receive her fragile, star-bright
gift from God.

WINTER WARMTH, *watercolour*

O God who gives us such
a fragile and precious gift
in the unfolding miracle
of human relationships.

Complex
Brilliant
Profound
Yet so easily
misunderstood
and abused.

When our relationships
become fraught
When they are drifting
apart
When they have lost
their light –

May we come back
to kneel at the foot of
Your wide cross –
and in looking up
rediscover You in the
centre of all true loving.

Waiting in Faith

His eyes moved slightly,
watching the men move,
leaving their homes in ones and twos –
the talk quiet, subdued,
the day like the men just stirring,
night and sleep still heavy in the air.

He'd been like them once.
Alive, vibrant, strong.
Look now at the twisted spine,
thin flesh stretched on thin bone,
big-hearted man shrivelled and dried,
as wasted and useless inside as the legs that
stuck strangely out, gauntly twitching.
And in his throat resentment hardened and bitterness stank.

The sun broke over the hills.
The darkness slipped away
and the earth began to bake in the warmth.
His wife, bent double, had to drag him into the shade.
He gritted his teeth
glancing away so he wouldn't see her face.
Closed his eyes to avoid her talk –
he hated the way she continued to share her life with him,
hated the way she doggedly fought to keep him alive
hated the way she kept on loving so he couldn't let go.
The sun reached its height in noon stillness.
He slipped into a sick sleep.

Thudding of feet
heavy breathing
the men burst into the quiet house.

Came as soon as we heard –
...Capernaeum...
...the man Jesus is back.
...don't know how long –
...if we run, we might make it...
He pounded his fists on the ground.

What? What's happening?

Grabbed a pot and sent it crashing into the wall.

What?

Sudden silence.
His wife quietly appeared,
eyes shining, a light in them.
He knew that look.

Oh no – no. No more. I'm not going.
Don't you dare make me.

She caught his thrashing arms, held him against her.

He's the only one who can heal you.
Do it for me.

All the hatred against her burst out –
he screamed and spat and hit her in rage.
She looked back to the doorway to the men who waited.

God help you,
she whispered to them
and moved aside.

He fought them,
thrashing viciously as they heaved him up high,
carrying him out of cool safety to the glare of the sun.

Suddenly afraid,
he reached back for his wife,
desperately begging her as she pulled away –
her face full of pain and hope
as he was bounced and jolted out of the staring village.

For God's sake, he pleaded.
Why are you doing this to me?

The run had to slow to a jog,
eventually to a walk.
The men were heaving
sweat running down their faces and backs.
No one spoke.
Time was crucial –
and the journey stretched long ahead.

The sun began to drop,
a coolness seeped through the heat.
The men wearily asked for final directions –
heaved him up once again.
So close now,
they pushed each other on,
beyond speech,
driven by faith.

Big crowd.
People stood solid and deep around the house.
They tried to get through –
were told to back off.

Disappointment hit hard.
Their limbs were aching, trembling;
skin raw from the chaffing of the pallet,
bruises swelling from his viciousness.

It didn't strike them as strange.
Having tried so hard
they were beyond normality.
They dragged and banged him up the side-steps to the roof,
pulled him over people's legs causing arguments and shouts.
With brute force they ripped off the leaf matting,
tying the strong vine around the pallet.
Muscles standing out,
backs straining,
they lowered him down into the startled gathering.

And the man found himself looking up at the Healer –
and after a moment looked away.
The Healer sighed and then looked up
to see the four men crouching around the hole.
Saw the exhaustion
the strain
the dried sweat.
Saw the strength of love that had driven them,
saw the pure and innocent and profound belief
that he was the One.

And slowly he smiled –
a smile that touched each of them.
And they knew they had been right.
The Healer bent and held the man's head,
forcing his eyes to meet his.

You are forgiven.

Pure power hit.

And the tired men watched the Healer's hands
grip harder,
tighter
until it seemed that they too were caught
into the healing,
became a part
of the holding.
And there was a strange sense of opening.
And for a moment the men glimpsed, felt, touched
something that was
stronger, deeper, fiercer than they had ever known.

But the man –
eaten by bitterness and fear –
couldn't bear to look at the Healer,
until the pain became too great
and in desperation
he sought the faces of his friends –
that in the moment of eternity
it was to their faith that he held.

But then around them,
a shocked murmur whipped.
Anger and suspicion broke the room
and suddenly the man was pulled back into the sharpness of the now.
These were his emotions being spoken out loud.
And at that moment
he became terrifyingly aware of powers against the Healer –
and his eyes shot back to the Healer's face
now turned to see the trouble –
a face full of strength and love
 – and anger
and despair.

And suddenly the man understood
and his fingers clenched tightly the hand of
the Healer –
and he returned the grip with strength.

The Healer looked down
and saw the man was ready.
And they both knew
the time had come.

Get up and walk.

The words were said.
The grip did not slacken.
The man stood and shakily
walked from the room.
Yet his eyes having found the Healer's,
never left his face,
until long after the crowd had moved in.
The men walked back slowly –
occasionally touching in the dark,
letting the night sky enable the extraordinary to linger on,
until they saw the lamps of home –
and a woman who was watching and waiting.

Seeing the five figures step out of the dark
a great sob caught in her throat,
and then it was that the wonder of God
burst from the man.
And with a tremendous shout that shattered
the stillness,
he ran to her,

I'm home!

*When my faith is barren
and I have difficulty in belief;
when I feel removed
from the fellowship
that others have;
when I can no longer
feel your presence
and do not know if you exist –*

*then in my wilderness
may I be carried
by the faith of my friends,
uplifted on their shoulders
until they bring me to your feet
O Christ –
and I find that I am home.*

The Touching Place

When it first started
it was put down to the heavy work in the fields,
then her family said it was the worry;
then, when it grew to alarming proportions,
the physicians said it was her diet –
and offered her strange potions,
herbs and poultices.
It was only much later
when it had not ceased
that the local people spoke out loud
and said what all were fearing –
she was diseased
she was unclean.
It was quite clear –
she was the cursed one.

She burnt with the guilt,
the horror,
of bearing such a terrible shame:
shame on her family,
shame on her community,
shame on her womanhood.

At first of course
exclusion was unbearable;
barely older than a girl
she was forced to live alone,
on the edge,
beside herself in loneliness.
But as time passed
she learnt to accept the bewilderment and shock.

And after the initial scandal
the community had quietened,
rejoicing secretly in their own well-being,
thankful that the curse was to be carried
by someone outside their own.

But over the years,
the lack of belonging
had left its mark.
The woman,
who as a girl had held so much potential,
had by exclusion
become silenced
subdued
isolated from all human warmth.
She was,
in truth,
the one who was untouched.

She rose that morning
as any other morning.
Gasped as the pain seared her back,
felt the warmth slipping away.
Slowly washed, cleansed,
spread fresh clothes.
But she knew in her heart
that the years of losing
had taken their toll.
Knew it in the bloodless pallor of her skin,
in the darkness of the shadows that dug
deep under her eyes.
Knew her life force had been drained away.
And deep down,
she knew her days were counted.

And suddenly
that morning,
she knew with utmost certainty,
that despite everything –
she wanted to live.
Never had life seemed so beautiful
as that moment of realisation –
when with every movement it slipped yet further from her.

So when she heard the noise,
the commotion, the excitement;
when she saw the fields and roads and hillsides
beginning to move with people –
she joined them,
sensed their delight.
Became, for the first time,
part of a crowd –
all strangers,
all intent on seeing the man.

She couldn't get close to the shore,
so many people.
Terrible disappointment.

But still she waited,
silently
in the glare of the sun,
the heat rising from her.
Stood with patience,
the acceptance that is born out of suffering.

Then the crowd moved.
A man was allowed through.
She craned to see –
why him?
But as he passed
she glimpsed his face –
and she pulled back,
gave him room.
Understood the pain, the fear,
recognised the look of one who was facing death.

Brief word with the healer,
then both were moving with urgency,
pushing their way back,
the fishermen begging the people to give them room.

And by one of those strange happenings
the crowd shifted
and the woman found herself being propelled forward,
carried by the momentum.

And suddenly,
the healer was so close –
a mere space from her
and a wild hope blazed in her –
if only!

If only she could just catch his hand
it would stop.
It would be over!

But then the crowd surged in,
a desperate mass of heaving arms and legs,
hot bodies and faces,
reaching out,
calling,
screaming,
pushing
and with a terrible cry,
realising she would miss him,
she forced all her strength into reaching –
twisting, grasping, her sinews stretching desperately,
as the fishermen struggled to hold them back.
And the fringe of his garment flickered past her fingers.

The shock hit her heart.
Thudded her back into the packed bodies.
Pounded terrifyingly through her
freeing the healing.
And she knew she was different.

But –
the healer knew.
Had felt the shock.
Turned.
Stopped.
Demanded a response.

Hidden amongst them,
she knew that he would find her.
She had his fire within.
He would without doubt recognise.
And as the crowd, sensing the change of mood,
fell silent,
her world disintegrated.

The outcast collapsed,
alone,
lost,
at his feet.
Exposed her shame to that strange and ignorant watchers.
And the silence grew
and grew,
until,
unable to bear it,
she raised her eyes to meet his.
And power burnt within her,
seemed to leap out to embrace them both.

And having waited for her,
his hand,
briefly,
touched her head.

She watched him go –
he who was the touching place –
surrounded by the fickle crowd.
And then,
just for a moment,
he turned –
and over the heads of the seething mass,
he smiled at her –
in recognition of one who truly was
His father's child.

And at peace,
she turned to face the blazing hills.

Oh Jesus –
how many times
I cry out to you

Oh Jesus –
how many times
I try to reach you

Oh Jesus –
how many times
I long for your healing.

Grant me your peace –
the peace that comes
beyond all understanding –
to surround,
fill,
uphold me –
so that I may rest in you.

INDIAN MARKET, *watercolour*

49

The Waiting of Jairus' Child

S he lay in the darkness breathing in the peace.
  She had no urge to reach out.
She was content to rest.
Content to be.

And so she waited.
Waited with the trust and the faith
that only the child-like possess.
Until she felt her heart beat fast
and knew that He drew near –
and her delight rippled through the dark
and she clapped her hands with excitement.

  I knew You would find me, she called
and she heard His answering laughter,
felt it surround her as she caught His fingers,
  I've been waiting for You!

And His answer came strong and gentle
  And I for you my friend.

For a long time she was content to rest with Him
and then she whispered
  I heard You call so clearly –
  But I couldn't reach You –
  it hurt so very much.

She felt His arms gather close.
Felt Him sigh in the dark,
Death is never easy, little one.

In the stillness they did not speak,
each knowing the pain that they had walked.
And her voice was very quiet.
I'm so glad You were there.

I am always there.
And again the certainty surrounded them.

She breathed in His presence –
and suddenly she was fully aware of
the next journey
and her soul could not wait.
Are we going now?

Perhaps.
She stopped and wondered why there was a choice.

But then it seemed to her
that for a moment her mother's arms held her
and she heard her father's voice
and the vividness of love warmed her.

I love them, she said and her voice was strong.

I know.
And they love you.

There was a pause.
Is that why we are waiting?
It's one of the reasons.

Again she rested and thought,
then turned quietly
  If I come back, will there be much pain?

  Yes.
  But much beauty too.

She thought slowly.
  Will You be there?
  I am always there.

He could feel her thoughts in the dark as she pondered His words.
But still she hesitated –
  Will I always hear You so clearly?

And His smile was warm.
  Now you find me in the calling
  of your friends
  in the gentleness of your father's hand,
  in the song of your mother's heart.
  Later you will discover me in different ways and different people.
  But I am always there, my little one –
  simply waiting for you to find me.

She looked at the choice of going on –
and everything in her
longed to answer the calling
and her soul was filled with delight.

And then she turned
and looked at going back –
thought of the agony and the suffering,
the sharpness of joy and the depth of loving.

And the child who walked and danced with the One
gathered her strength and breathed God in.

I am ready, she said simply.
I am ready to come back.

And the grip on her hand grew stronger
and held tight.
From far away she heard the voice
she loved so well.
She stood tall as the coldness shot towards her
pierced the darkness,
pierced her small body,
pierced her heart.
But unafraid,
she took the pain within
and in utter trust leaped towards the voice.

And icy air rushed into her lungs
and she breathed long and deep at the pain –
and the beauty –
of life.
Slowly her eyes opened into this world
and she looked up at the face of the One
who in her soul,
she knew so well.

Her thin arms reached up
to wind around His neck
as she laid her head against His face.

Jesus! My Jesus!
I'm home.

Not all the sermons
not all the texts
not all the theologies
can rid the deeply hidden fear
that is the passage of death.

May the certainty of dying
sharpen the desire to live.

May the discovery of You, God
transform the journey.

And may I grow in child-like trust
to rest my soul in Jesus –
and thus make life worth living –
and death but a step
to You.

SUMMER SUNSHINE, *Pastel*

One out of Ten

There was a strange comradeship amongst the ten of them.
Of course they fought and squabbled,
fell out amongst themselves.
But when one stumbled
he would be carried between them.
When one could not see,
the others became his eyes.
When one could not bear the deadness
the others understood,
knowing what each went through.

At the end of the day it was them against the world.
Living together, dying together, burying their own,
broken and numb against a world of feeling.

In a world that was riddled with barriers
they were a group that had learnt to accept each other –
because they had a common exclusion and a common fate.
They shared the same disease that killed all feeling –
the taken-for-granted glory of the body.

They lived on the outskirts of the village,
in the scrap land where no one journeyed.
Sometimes they would sit on the rubbish heap
and watch the children play,
their legs showering the dust as they chased;
sometimes they caught a frightened smile
from one of the women leaving them food;
very occasionally they heard news of far away homes –
a wedding,
a death,
a birth.

And always they carried the hatred of the bell of fear,
the hatred of calling out *unclean* to warn the healthy away.
And always, at all times,
the desperate longing to be whole,
to be normal,
to be loved.

It was enough to break the soul.
Overwhelming hopelessness.

They heard the rumour that he was coming,
so they slipped and struggled and pulled each other
to the brink of the hill.
Within sight of the road
yet far enough away to escape the stone throwing.

He was unmistakable and unmissable.
Instinctively they set up their wail.
Both eerie and haunting on the air.
The group of men with him glanced and carried on
but the One in their midst stopped and turned to them.

Immediately a renewed urgency swept through them
as sudden hope flared.

  Jesus! Master! Have mercy on us!
the call started to be picked up by them all.

And as each joined in, each in their own way begging,
each offering themselves for healing,
a tremendous power could be felt –
strengthening and emboldening them.

The One stepped towards them.
And in that movement, the invisible bonds of the disease were broken.

As he came closer,
the heat poured through them –
a burning fire that scorched into their numbed bodies,
sent fire sensations through fingers and toes,
legs and faces that had been long dead.

Go and show yourselves to the priests!
His voice sent the fire soaring inside.

Incredulous at what was happening the group went wild,
shouting and laughing and crying
as forgotten glory and pain rippled through them.

They ran delirious to the village,
calling to all to come out and see them
leaping and hurtling through the streets.

And then one of them stopped,
    Wait! I want to go back!

They were laughing too much to listen,
unable to stop, simply desperate to get home.

    Wait! he called,
but they ran on, starting to leave the group,
each heading for his own village.
He turned and ran back,
scrambled up the hill and over the brink,
calling to the group still on the road.
By the time he caught them he was breathless.
The excitement shining through him, he pushed through to the One.
Couldn't stop.
Flung his arms around him,
kissed his face and hands
and finally kneeling on the ground, his feet.

Thank you! Thank you! Thank you!

The men were laughing around him,
reaching out to touch him,
the noise and exhilaration setting the air alight.

Where are the others? the One asked.
The man tried to catch his breath and steady his heart –
I had to come back!
Had to thank you!

The One took in the different accent.
Looked down into the face of utter love upturned to him,
alive with hope, with life, with bursting delight –

and he pulled him to his feet.
Go home my friend.
Your faith has made you well.

The man clutched him tightly – and then let go.
Started to walk the long walk home
but couldn't control the amazing feeling inside – and broke into a run.

His head back, his lungs full of clean air,
he ran with sheer joy – before suddenly turning back he called

I shall never forget you!
I will thank God all my life for you!

And in the distance,
the One raised His arms to him –
and the reply came echoing back –

And I for you my friend –
and I for you!

O God of such abundant gifts –

If I have the gift of science
keep me open
to use my skill.

If I have the gift of finance
keep me compassionate
to share my gold.

If I have the gift of vision
keep me inspired
to ignite imagination.

And to those who long for healing
may I become
the touch of Christ.

WALK THROUGH THE WOODS, *watercolour*

Bondage Breaker

I nside his mind
splintered thoughts chased unendingly
around the vast tunnels.
Disjointed beginnings that had no end.
No clarity, no fruition.

No one understood –
the self destruction when his thoughts tried to connect
the mutilation of rage
the power of violence.

When panic from the angers overwhelmed
and the climax had been reached,
then it was that the darkness slipped in and took over.
Settled in his mind
and rooted down into his heart.
Fed and ate upon the hatred within,
consumed,
ruled.

He learnt at an early age the weapon of fear.
Saw it in children's eyes
watching, absorbing, transfixed by him.
Saw it deeper in adults –
parents, community.
Those who loved and offered friendship
he found he could break.

The darkness moved him from one to another.
Clever, cunning, manipulative.
And always, ruthlessly destructive.

Sometimes he caught a glimpse of something –
a chance echo on the breeze fleetingly held a memory –
and then he would run,
frantically, blindly,
crashing back to the tombs.

As the darkness poured over him –
throwing him from side to side
pounding him onto the walls
repeatedly breaking his body
until pain exploded.
Haunted and possessed,
his eyes seeing distorted dreams reaching to take him –
he ran howling at the dead of night.

Beyond human knowledge.
Beyond human love.
Beyond.

Until the One came.

Hiding in the darkness of the tombs
the possessed watched the boat draw nearer.
And a terrible laughter contorted him.
He flung himself onto the rocks.
Leaping and twisting in the air
grotesquely silhouetted,
the noise reverberated from rock to rock,
causing him to clap his hands over his ears
as the shrieks rose higher and higher
from the dark cavern of his mouth.

Saw the startled faces of the fishermen
upturned to see the noise.
And at that moment
He who was the One connected and locked into the man.
Penetrated through the rushing tunnels
the density of rooted evil;
sent the dark screaming in rage.

Propelled by the terrorising darkness
the man threw himself off the rocks
screaming foulness,
raw violence hell-bound,
solely focused on the One –
his hands stretching to obey the inner command to destroy.

Suddenly he stopped.

The One had no fear.

Instead He blazed –
blazed with an anger such as the dark had never seen.
Power more fearful than any the dark possessed.

   Get out!
His voice ripped.
The man backed and cowered gibbering out a string of words.

The One strode over him
sending him into paralysed whimpers of fear

   Your name!

Forcing the man's head up to look at Him

   Tell me your name!

Inside the dark recesses
the names raced
tripping over each other
soured and fouled.
But the eyes still held –
pulling something out of the darkness.

Legion, the man whispered. *So many inside me.*

And the laughter shrieked out into the One's face.

Leave him!

The command gripped the darkness and pulled.

The man opened his mouth
and screamed –
a human scream that was beyond bearing
as the darkness dragged his heart through the chaos of insanity.
He crawled desperately into the One's arms,
pulling them repeatedly around himself,
hiding in Him as the darkness poured into the nearby pigs,
unearthly shrieks filling the air
as they rushed to the water.

He buried his head,
holding the One's hands across his face,
clinging, clawing into Him.

And the One held tight.

It's over.
It's over.

Later
the crowds came –
eager fascination staring at the changed man
whispers, fingers pointing.
But he did not move –
stayed close to the One
eyes following His face.

But then,
the uneasy crowd asked He who was the One
to go.
And so
the fire was scuffed over,
the boat pushed out,
the men prepared to move on.
The man watched the One climb aboard
and his heart broke inside.
He pushed through the water,
caught on to Him
holding Him fiercely, forgetting his strength.

Don't!
Don't leave me. Please!
Take me with you.

The tears poured down his scarred face.

Don't leave me.
Not now that I've found you.

The One looked down at the matt of bloodied hair,
the battered and defaced body,
the extraordinary violence.

Looked up at the hills and slowly took in the empty tombs.
Saw the awkward muttering crowd.
Finally looked back at the man.

He spoke very gently.

I need you to stay.
Tell your people.
Be the man of God here – for me.

The man knew it was true.
He had to be left behind.
And he had to let go.

But then as the boat pulled out the One took
the man's huge maimed hands,
turned the palms upwards and tenderly kissed them.

I am always with you.
I shall never let you go.

The man watched until he could see the boat no more,
his arms stretched wide open
reaching out to the One.

The end had found the beginning.

O God
I find there are so many bonds
that slip silently into my life,
gathering their hold on me
before I am aware.

And then I cannot find you
for they push me away
and block out your truth.

When I am submerged and held down
help me remember
the sheer power of Jesus Christ,
so much stronger
so much fiercer
so much greater
than any force that diminishes and destroys.

I hold fast to you Jesus –
my beginning and my end.

WESTERN FJORDS, NORWAY, *watercolour*

Broken Touch

Inside the city the atmosphere intensified.
The streets,
normally adequate for trade,
were packed to overflowing.
Tempers were heated;
the shade shimmered.
Standing too close,
pressed into strangers' arms and faces and bodies.
Hard for men used to space and solitude.

The man of the country
made the hand-over as promised and
secured the contract.
He left the trading place
pushing his way back into the heaving streets.
Felt the regular rhythm shake the ground
long before he heard the shouts.

God – what a day for crucifixions.

Resented the way the Romans enforced their superiority –
today of all days.
The crowd tried to move apart
but it was almost impossible –
there was barely room for anyone to pass
let alone a death-party.

He was pushed back by the foremost soldier
but there was nowhere to go
and the man found himself staring face to face with him –
a young soldier, same age as his own sons –
but this was a youth with power
because he held a whip
and fingered cold steel.
And surprisingly,
the countryman saw fear in the soldier's eyes.

His attention was caught.
Death was frequent here.
Soldiers were obeyed.

And then, he heard a whisper –
a name quivered through the crowd
and the victim came into sight
flanked closely by nervous soldiers.
And the wailing of the women
silenced the eager crowd.

Strange thing about victims –
they both fascinate and horrify.
Thus it was with the countryman –
rapidly taking in the bloodied back,
the soldiers jest of a crown,
the ashen face –
a strong, good face.

Uncomfortable
he looked away quickly
so felt, rather than saw,
the ominous thud as the victim sprawled
through the dust.

Gasp of the crowd pressing to see,
panic of soldiers suddenly surrounded.
A fuse about to be lit.

An order snapped from the centurion.
Military discipline,
pulled together by the older man in charge.

> *Find someone to carry the cross.*
> *And for God's sake get him on his feet.*

Immediately in front of the countryman's gaze
the young soldier surfaced.

> *You! Carry it!*

Amazing how quickly the over-packed street
moved back leaving the man surrounded by space.
He stared
totally astounded.

> *I said carry it!* the soldier spat.

His voice verging on hysteria.

Sickness surged into the countryman's mouth
filled him with repugnance.
He could not bring his hands,
hands used to country birth and death,
to touch the soldiers' way of destruction.

The whip lashed out
driven by fear.
But the soldier had acted through lack of knowledge of man.

Despite being big,
the countryman moved with speed.
Catching the thong unexpectedly,
he pulled the soldier against him in one swift movement,
hands on his throat
the grip tightening as the countryman blazed with fury.

Strong hands tore him away.
The centurion stood between them.

Man of the fields.
Man of war.
Men from different lands,
different religions
measured each other.

Slowly the centurion bent and picked up the cross,
his eyes never leaving the countryman.
He held it out
and the battle flared between them.

Carry it.

His skin recoiling at the touch
jaw clenched
the countryman took the means of death,
eyes grinding into the centurion's
as he pushed past him.

The centurion's hand stopped him.
He spoke quietly.

Behind him.

And there was a fleeting moment of compassion
that bewildered the countryman.

A sharp order
and the party moved.
Only this time
the victim was held between two soldiers
and the cross carried by the man of earth.

At first
the anger scorched through the countryman
churned inside and burnt him.
But gradually, almost imperceptibly
his thoughts moved from himself
to the one whose cross he carried.

His eyes fixed rigidly to the ground
the man slowly became aware
that he was placing his feet
in the footsteps of the victim.
And it was at that moment
when the cross became unbearably heavy
and tiredness registered
that the wave hit him.
Sorrow such as he had never experienced.

It flooded him and broke him.

Unwittingly
a terrible sob burst through his clenched teeth.
As the cross slipped,
he shook uncontrollably and collapsed sideways.

Strong hands caught him.
Pulled him upright,
steadied him for the final climb.
Without a word,
the centurion stood beside him.

Legs trembling,
he could sense, could smell,
the awfulness of the place that came closer.

O God, help me, he whispered again and again.

God help me.
God help me.

His eyes fixed on the victim's feet,
he was terrified by the immediacy
of what was about to happen,
terrified that in a moment it would be over
and he would have to lift his head and walk away
knowing that he had experienced
something beyond his explanation.
Terrified that he would have to abandon
the person who had trod the way before him.

And then the wasteland was there.
Soldiers moving quickly to quiet orders.

His role finished
the countryman finally raised his head,
forced himself to look around,
absorb reality
before slowly bringing his gaze to the victim's face.

And at last,
after a journey such as none had ever trod,
a journey that was to forge the way
across a thousand centuries
and be echoed through worlds beyond knowing,
their eyes met.
The journey of such overwhelming grief,
such power
such intimacy
lay open between them.

And in the agony of death
the victim reached out;
broken fingers touched the ruggedness of
the countryman's face.

And the man of the fields
discovered that which he had not known
he was waiting for.

He didn't stay.
He had been the first,
caught unknowingly into the heart of events
to change life and death.

It was only now,
standing face to face with the cross,
that he understood.

Death was not the end of this man!
It was, quite simply, the beginning.

As he turned away,
he saw the centurion quietly watching.

And across the crucifixion
He who was the Promise
reached unbound between them.

There are times in my life God
when I cannot carry your cross.
It is too heavy.
And my heart has not
the fire within.

At these moments
when my eyes are fixed
on the ground
and cannot see ahead,
help me to see
the worn and roughened
feet of Jesus
quietly walking just before me.

Then as I place my small step
after Him,
I realise the way I tread
has already been walked
by Christ.

I am not alone.
Thank God –
I am not alone.

AUTUMN WOODS, *watercolour*

A. D. ASKEW

An Ordinary Death

He found his eyes closing
only to be swept into horrific nightmares
of screams and torture.
Woke with his body soaked in sweat,
his lungs seized up, fighting to breathe.

He didn't know whether it was better
to be alive in this hell-hole
or to have his life end.

Knew he would be called today.
Yesterday the others with whom he had been
sentenced had been crucified.
Heard the shouts, the calls to each other as
the soldiers passed outside;
heard the door open,
the wail inside becoming deafening;
heard the soldiers' feet stop
in front of him.
Rough hands, everyday business,
brusqueness of death.

His heart raced inside
as they dragged him over the flagstones,
swearing as he slipped,
telling him to shut it,
as his name was filed
before rapidly, with bewildering precision,
they were moving.

Recognised the other prisoner –
had seen him working the crowds.
Had once been frightened off by him,
told to keep to his own patch
or else he'd be sorted.
Even now,
as they were pushed along the familiar stones,
paths being trodden for the last time,
the other prisoner did not acknowledge him.

It was as if he,
a cheap ordinary little robber,
had no right to share even the same
death sentence as this brute.

So desperately afraid.
And there was no one there to hold on to.
He was dying alone and unloved.

At the place
there was some hold up.
He glanced without meaning to
at the tin of long nails.
His empty stomach heaved
as his body contracted.
Went into uncontrollable rigours.

The soldiers held him firm.
Had seen this a thousand times.
More concerned with getting the third one done quickly,
before there was trouble.

Finally he came.
The third prisoner.
Heavy escort.
The soldiers silently formed a blockade
separating prisoners from crowd.

Somehow,
having another one there
helped ease the fear.
He slowly surfaced
became aware of the tenseness.
Caught a name muttered among the soldiers
and everything in him surged alive.

Wait! He'd worked the people whilst this man talked.
Marvellous thieving opportunity.
He'd stopped for a while and actually sat and enjoyed listening.

This man,
so brilliant and warm and funny,
had made him laugh out loud with the crowd;
for a moment it seemed as if everyone
was friends.
Remembering back,
it had been one of his happiest moments.

And now
on this terrible day of death
when the fear of what was about to happen
pounded through his head,
this man
who had been to him such a wondrous,
life-filled distant figure,
was being nailed up next to him to die.

The petty thief
the commonest man who had lived his life in
mediocrity
was stunned.
Here was he,
the lowest of the pack,
being allowed to share death with this man.

It was the greatest honour that earth could
have given him.

The bare hill behind,
the soldiers before,
he watched the man being crucified first.
He looked so terribly humble
as he was stretched out on the ground;
the pain shattering his face
as the soldiers did their job;
the desperate gasp to breathe
as he was raised up.

And the nightmares rushed back
as the soldiers turned to him
and pushed him down.
Everything within fought to survive –
until being held down by the sheer weight of men,
his head was forced up
and he saw the face of Jesus
looking down upon him.

Through the screams,
he held onto that face.

The job was finished.
Swiftly and with no trouble, the three had been crucified.
Only time needed now to complete the job.

A remnant of the soldiers remained –
warning off those who spat,
pushing away those that came too close.
Until suddenly the brutal prisoner spoke.
Even in death there was something so utterly bestial in him.
He tore out and mocked the Christ,
his words jarring.

Wracked by the weight of the piercing hanging,
in a midst of pain,
the robber found himself replying.
For the first time in his life
he spoke out against the hatred.
Answered strongly, with utter clarity.
He had nothing more to fear.

Then his eyes turned to the Christ.
And he found in the gathering dark
that the face echoing his own agony
was still filled with the greatness of gentleness.

Remember me Jesus, whispered the robber,
when you come in your kingly power.

And the Christ smiled at him –
a smile so full of love
totally concentrating just on him,
as if they were long-time friends,
not strangers waiting to die,
that the robber forgot about death
and smiled back.

Today you will be with me in Paradise.

The light had gone from the sky.
Torches had to be lit.
The darkness seemed to be rushing towards them.
He realised that everything in him was dying,
that his life was finally over.

As his breathing became too hard
and his heart strove to beat
the thief turned his head
so that his last moments would be filled
with the face of Jesus.
He saw the piercing cry –
and knew he could now go.
As hope stepped ahead
his own heart
gave the final slow flicker.

No one there noticed the last breath of the unnoticeable little robber
who had lived such a common life
and had died such a glorious and privileged death.

So no one noticed that before he left this life
his face was transformed
for it had been touched by infinite love.

And no one noticed that at the very last,
he lifted up his head in greeting –
as he who was the least
ran to the One
who waited for him.

At times I feel so very ordinary.
In being belittled
I become too small
to handle the big issues
and too insignificant
to make a contribution.
No one takes me seriously.

And then I remember Jesus
who thinks I am so special
so unique
so utterly precious
that He stretched out His arms –
and broke death –
for me.

May I,
who am so loved by Christ,
never cease to cherish others –
so that they too
can grow and deepen
into the loveliness of God.

LIGHT ON THE FJORD, NORWAY, **pastel**

A. D. ASKEW

Man of Power

He had loved the Man for such a long time.
A steady love that had grown and deepened
to become the basis of his life.

Of course over these last few years
there had been rumours of this Man in the Council;
of course,
in the splendour of his house,
there was talk of him after business was completed.
Of course, being one of the men of power,
he knew what was happening.
And because he was a man of faith,
an older man trusted and revered not because of his
wealth but for his mind,
he had journeyed through the heat in order
to sit and listen and absorb this Galilean.

And to his amazement
he had found himself gripped by the words,
the power of the speech,
the simpleness and profundity.

He had a deep understanding and intellectual mind –
constantly searching,
set alight by new concepts and ideas.
As he listened to the Man
he struggled to take in the vastness,
the possibilities being shown.

He was challenged
disturbed
inspired
and delighted by what he found.

His presence there did not go unnoticed.
The Man's followers had recognised him,
made a point of acknowledging him.
And discreetly
he had met the Man.
Been welcomed to join them for supper at one
of the local homes.

He was surprised
by the strength of the handshake,
the openness and ease,
the tremendous power with which the Man talked as they ate.
Surprised by the laughter,
the magnetism,
the sheer charisma.

He had journeyed home the next day.
Inside him wild and impossible thoughts and feelings
were racing.
For the first time in his life,
he felt as if he had touched upon the
inner meaning of God.

And so he began his journey.

But now Jerusalem was overflowing –
Passover was always a fraught time.
Too many people in too small a space.
Ideal for rabble raising and uprisings.

It did not surprise him to see the movements of the crowds
following the Man.
The wild cheering,
the strange ability of massed people to sense and hone in
upon a focus point.
What worried him was the attitude of the leaders,
both Jewish and Roman.
He felt that the Council was becoming
manipulated from a number of quarters.

He was uneasy that the Man,
who had already started unprecedented
anger in the Temple,
would somehow become the public's target.
Extra soldiers were being drafted in each day,
rumours were circulating of insurrections,
authority's temper was taut.

He heard the quiet knock on the door
long after the Passover had been celebrated.
One of the Man's followers slipped into the house –
his face drawn with fear.

The follower told him of their meal –
how they had been laughing and boasting of the future,
how the Man had been silent.
How He had taken bread and wine
and talked of death and betrayal.

How the men,
young in their knowledge of human nature,
had not understood.
How they had gone out into the garden
and the Man had seemed restless.
And then in the peace of the night the soldiers had come –
and they had taken Him away.
How terrified they were –
everyone running and hiding.

The older man listened without interrupting –
saw it all unfold before him.
Felt the terror of the follower overflow.
No sooner had he finished
then a quiet knock came again at the door.
The follower went rigid.
Warily the older man listened to his servant's tread,
the murmur of the voices,
the feet drawing nearer.

It was a summons to the Council.
To be called at this hour meant only one thing –
dark business being done.

He climbed to the high priest's house
with fear beyond human experience.

Never had he seen such anger, such hatred,
as was gathered within its walls.
Men with whom he had worked, debated, prayed with,
seemed to be overtaken by such vehemence
that reason and faith –
and God –
were forgotten in a great wave of darkness.

And at the centre of their rage stood the Man;
His skin now the sick grey of death,
His body bruising and discoloured from beatings,
His carpenter's hands fiercely bound.

The older man felt the ground move beneath him.
A terrible whiplash of pain shot across his chest
and into his fingers.
The Man, in the midst of this brutality,
looked so unbearably young,
so unbearably sad.
As if the light had already been stamped out.

The clamour grew and grew
until he could bear no more.
Trembling,
he made his way through the fury of the room
to stand beside the Man.
And the Man smiled at him with such an unbearable sweetness.

And for a moment,
the older man's presence brought stillness.
As he spoke
God could be felt.
It seemed as if he would be heard
and the mood would change.

But then a voice sliced across his.
And the wave,
momentarily held back,
broke.
The noise was deafening
as the assembled men of faith
reached the depth of human depravity
and death was released.

He was knocked aside
as the victim was pushed from the room
to be dragged back and forth in the pale light
between the powers-that-be.

Clutching the pain in his chest,
he wiped a shaking hand across his face.
He knew he had to do something
but felt paralysed.

He didn't seem able to move quickly enough,
to think quickly enough.
Still clinging to the hope that something would
happen to stop the nightmare.
But no one was listening.
Everyone was caught in this frenzied power.
It was all so very quick.
In the space of nothing it was over.
He followed, horrified, to the place of execution.

The older leader, who was so powerful,
and who had found such faith,
stood broken.
As the shadows beat angrily across the sky
he saw again and again in his mind's eye
the image of the Man breaking warm bread,
offering blood red wine.

O God.
What have I done?

O God.
What have I not done?

He knew,
long before the soldiers confirmed
that it was finished.

His heart too heavy to carry
he wearily walked back to the scene of betrayal.
Tried to draw himself up as he was admitted.
In the glooming of the room
the Governor's eyes met his.
They both knew.
They both had tried but had not done enough.

And they looked away from each other.

The permission granted
he walked, stumbled that terrible route.
Handed the paper of authority over to the soldiers.
The Man,
dead and cold,
was cut down.

The older man carried Him to his own tomb
empty and waiting in the night.

Holding the body in the dark
the man suddenly could bear no more.
Bending his head over the broken corpse
he gathered it into his arms
and sobbed and sobbed.

He sat at the window of his house
watching the day dawn and fall.
He could not bear to go on living –
not without Him.

So when the news came,
on flying feet and gasping breath
Joseph of Arimathea
stared in sheer wonder.

He did not go to his tomb.
He knew there was no need.
A new way had been opened.

And suddenly he had the strangest feeling that the
Man, the Christ,
was at his door.
He ran to it and flung it open,
his face radiant with love.

And the noise and the clamour of a seething city
surrounded him.
Plunged into disappointment,
he searched for the face he loved in the mass of people.
And as he searched,
the image of bread and wine came vividly to him.

   O God, he whispered, *now I understand!*

And at that moment,
as he opened his whole being to the wonder of God,
a face in the crowd momentarily turned to him.
And the laughing Christ
held out His hand –
and beckoned him into the waiting world.

SUDDEN SUNSHINE, *pastel*

Almighty God,

*Oh so beyond words
yet intimately
and magnificently revealed
in Christ Jesus.*

*You have called each of us
to live for you.*

*May I live with passion the life
you have given me,
may my heart be filled
with your gentleness,
may I share all that is Christ
with those whom I meet.*

*And may I live and work,
breathe and die
to your eternal praise
and glory.*

Amen.

Bible References

The Recognition – Luke, ch. 2

The Desert Waiting – John, ch. 4

A Matter of Minutes – John, ch. 9

Unseen Gift – Luke, ch. 10

Waiting in Faith – Matthew, ch. 9; Mark, ch. 2; Luke, ch. 5

The Touching Place – Matthew, ch. 9; Mark, ch. 5; Luke, ch. 8

The Waiting of Jairus' Child
Matthew, ch. 9; Mark, ch. 5; Luke, ch. 8

One out of Ten – Luke, ch. 17

Bondage Breaker – Mark, ch.5; Luke, ch. 8; (Matthew, ch. 8)

Broken Touch – Matthew, ch. 27; Mark, ch. 15; Luke, ch. 23

An Ordinary Death – Luke, ch. 23

Man of Power
Luke, ch. 23; Matthew, ch. 27; Mark, ch. 15; John, ch. 19

Leprosy Mission contact addresses and telephone numbers

TLM International
80 Windmill Road
Brentford
Middlesex TW8 0QH
United Kingdom
Tel: 020 8569 7292
Fax: 020 8569 7808
friends@tlmint.org
www.leprosymission.org

TLM Trading Limited
PO Box 212
Peterborough PE2 5GD
UK
Tel: 01733 239252
Fax: 01733 239258
tlmtrading@dial.pipex.com
www.tlmtrading.com

TLM Africa Regional Office
PO Box HG 893
Highlands
Harare, Zimbabwe
Tel: 263 4 733709
Fax: 263 4 721166
ertlmaro@icon.co.zw

TLM Australia
PO Box 293
37 Ellingworth Parade
Box Hill
Victoria 3128
Australia
Tel: 61 39890 0577
Fax: 61 39890 0550
tlmaust@leprosymission.org.au
www.leprosymission.org.au

**TLM Belgium
(Leprazending)**
PO Box 20
1800 Vilvoorde
Belgium
Tel: 32 22519983
Fax: 32 22519983
leprazending@online.be

TLM Canada
75 The Donway West
Suite 1410
North York
Ontario M3C 2E9
Canada
Tel: 1 416 4413618
Fax: 1 416 4410203
tlm@tlmcanada.org
www.tlmcanada.org

TLM Denmark
Skindergade 29 A
1.DK - 1159 Copenhagen
Denmark
Tel: 45 331 18642
Fax: 45 331 18645
lepra@lepra.dk
www.lepra.dk

**TLM England & Wales,
Channel Islands & Isle of Man**
Goldhay Way
Orton Goldhay
Peterborough PE2 5GZ
United Kingdom
Tel: 01733 370505
Fax: 01733 370960
post@tlmew.org.uk
www.leprosymission.org.uk

TLM Finland
Hakolahdentie 32 A 4
00200 Helsinki
Finland
Tel: 358 9 692 3690
Fax: 358 9 692 4323
eeva-liisa.moilanen
@kolumbus.fi

TLM France
BP 186
63204 Riom Cedex
France
Tel: 33 473 387660
Fax: 33 473 387660

TLM Germany
Kuferstrasse 12
73728 Esslingen
Germany
Tel: 49 711 353 072
Fax: 49 711 350 8412
LEPRA-Mission@t-online.de
www.lepramission.de

TLM Hong Kong
GPO Box 380
Central Hong Kong
Hong Kong
Tel: 85 228056362
Fax: 85 228056397
tlmhk@netvigator.com

TLM Hungary
Alagi Ter 13
H-1151 Budapest
Hungary

TLM India Regional Office
CNI Bhavan
16 Pandit Pant Marg
Delhi 110 001
India
Tel: 91 11 371 6920
Fax: 91 11 371 0803
tlmindia@del2.vsnl.net.in

TLM Italy
Via Adda 13
05100 Terni
Italy
Tel: 39 7448 11218
arpe@seinet.it

TLM Netherlands
Postbus 902
7301 BD Apeldoorn
Netherlands
Tel: 31 55 3558535
Fax: 31 55 3554772
leprazending.nl@inter.nl.net

TLM New Zealand
P O Box 10-227
Auckland
New Zealand
Tel: 64 9 630 2818
Fax: 64 9 630 0784
enquiries@tlmnz.org.nz

TLM Northern Ireland
Leprosy House
44 Ulsterville Avenue
Belfast BT9 7AQ
N Ireland
Tel: 02890 381937
Fax: 01232 381842
ColinF@tlm-ni.org
www.tlm-ni.org

TLM Norway
PO Box 2347
Solli
Arbingst. 11N 0201
Oslo, Norway
Tel: 47 2243 8110
Fax: 47 2243 8730
gaute.hetland
@bistandsnemnda.no

TLM Portugal
Casa Adelina
Sitio do Poio
8500 Portimao
Portugal
Tel: 351 82 471180
Fax: 351 82 471516
coaa@mail.telepac.pt

TLM Republic of Ireland
5 St James Terrace
Clonskeagh Road
Dublin 6
Republic of Ireland
Tel: 353 126 98804
Fax: 353 126 98804
106125.365
@compuserve.com

TLM Scotland
89 Barnton Street
Stirling FK8 1HJ
Scotland
Tel: 01786 449 266
Fax: 01786 449 766
lindatodd@compuserve.com
www.biggar-net.co.uk
/tlmscotland

TLM South East Asia
6001 Beach Road
#08-06 Golden Mile Tower
199589 Singapore
Tel: 65 294 0137
Fax: 65 294 7663
pdsamson@tlmsea.com.sg

TLM Southern Africa
Private Bag X06
Lyndhurst 2106
Johannesburg, S. Africa
Tel: 27 11 440 6323
Fax: 27 11 440 6324
leprosy@infonet.co.za

TLM Spain
Apartado de Correos
51.332CP
28080 Madrid, Spain
Tel: 34 91 594 5105
Fax: 34 91 594 5105
mundosolidari
@mx3.redestb.es

TLM Sweden
Box 145
S-692 23 Kumla, Sweden
Tel: 46 19 583790
Fax: 46 19 583741
lepra@algonet.se

TLM Switzerland
Chemin de Rechoz 3
CH-1027 Lonay/Vaud
Switzerland
Tel: 41 21 8015081
Fax: 41 21 8031948
mecl@bluewin.ch
www.lepramission.ch

TLM Zimbabwe
PO Box BE 200
Belvedere
Harare
Zimbabwe
Tel: 263 4 741817
tlmzim@tlmzim.icon.co.zw

ALM International
1 ALM Way
Greenville
S C 29601
USA
Tel: 1 864 271 7040
Fax: 1 864 271 7062
amlep@leprosy.org

SUMMER IN NORWAY, pastel

The Leprosy Mission Response Card

Hilary Faith Jones is a relatively new author writing poetry that gets to the heart of the Christian faith. Her books are illustrated with Eddie Askew's sketches and paintings. Eddie Askew is a popular Christian author, artist and retreat leader. Together their books raise funds for The Leprosy Mission to help people affected by leprosy. They are available from The Leprosy Mission in your own country or from TLM Trading Limited in the UK as well as most good Christian book shops.

TLM Trading Limited, owned by The Leprosy Mission, seeks to create employment by purchasing goods from rehabilitation centres and craft workshops who employ people affected by leprosy. These goods are sold along with gifts, cards and books to raise funds for The Leprosy Mission.

Please send me information about: - (please tick)

- [ ] The Leprosy Mission's mail order catalogue
- [ ] The Leprosy Mission's work
- [ ] Prayer support
- [ ] Sending a regular gift by automatic payment, standing order, or direct debit to support The Leprosy Mission
- [ ] Tax efficient ways of supporting The Leprosy Mission
- [ ] Service Overseas with The Leprosy Mission

Credit Card Sales and enquires: Tel: 01733 239252
Fax: 01733 239258
E-mail address: tlmtrading@dial.pipex.com

Titles by Hilary Faith Jones	Order code
Awakenings	03030
Waiting For Jesus	03031
Titles by Eddie Askew	
A Silence and a Shouting	03001
Disguises of Love	03002
Many Voices One Voice	03003
No Strange Land	03004
Facing The Storm	03005
Breaking the Rules	03006
Cross Purposes	03000
Slower than Butterflies (Book)	03024
Slower Than Butterflies (Audio Cassette)	20200
Music on the Wind	03025
Edge of Daylight (Hardback)	03026
Edge of Daylight (Paperback)	03027

Name .... Title ....

Address...

....

Post Code..................... Country............... Source Code 252

TLM Trading Limited
P.O. Box 212
Peterborough
PE2 5GD
United Kingdom

Please use your local Leprosy Mission address if you prefer, see page 99.

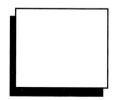